Fantasy Phonics
Activity Book

Created and Written by Caroline Petherbridge

Illustrated by Helen Prole

This edition published 2006 BCA,
by arrangement with Sparkle Education Limited

Created and written by Caroline Petherbridge

Production by Sally Humphrey

Illustrated by Helen Prole

Layout and design Sparkle Education Limited, The Fairway, Bush Fair,
Harlow CM18 6LY
www.sparkle-education.co.uk

ISBN: 1 85781 856 3

Printed in China by CTPS

Fantasy Phonics

an enchanting way to learn

The Fantasy Phonics range is built around the imaginary and magical world of Fantasyland – a place that taps into children's favourite childhood fantasies. Each letter of the alphabet is represented by a character or object that appeals to children; for when a child's imagination is captured and they are enjoying themselves, then they will learn.

Children should colour all the objects on a page that start with the correct letter sound. Then they can practise writing the letter in both its lower and upper case forms. The starting dots and direction arrows are provided to ensure that children are forming their letters correctly.

Aa

Handwriting Practice

Bb

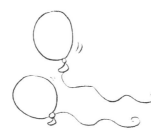

Colour all the pictures that start with the sound

b

Handwriting Practice

b

B

Cc

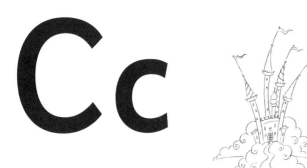

Colour all the pictures that start with the sound

c

Handwriting Practice

Dd

Colour all the pictures that start with the sound
d

Handwriting Practice

d

D

Ee

  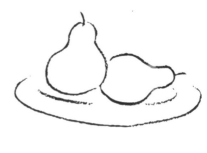

Handwriting Practice

Ff

Colour all the pictures that start with the sound
f

Handwriting Practice

Gg

Colour all the pictures that start with the sound

g

  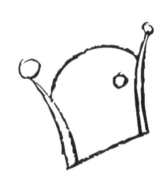

Handwriting Practice

Hh

Colour all the pictures that start with the sound **h**

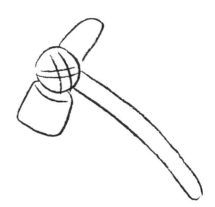

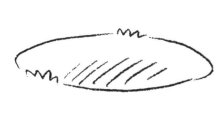

Handwriting Practice

Ii

Handwriting Practice

i

i

Jj

Handwriting Practice

Kk

Colour all the pictures that start with the sound
k

Handwriting Practice

k

k

L l

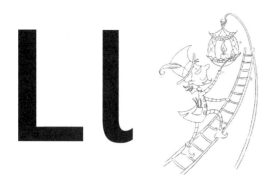

Colour all the pictures
that start with the sound
l

Handwriting Practice

M m

Handwriting Practice

m

M

Nn

Handwriting Practice

n

N

Oo

Colour all the pictures that start with the sound

o

Handwriting Practice

P p

Colour all the pictures that start with the sound

p

Handwriting Practice

Q q

Handwriting Practice

Rr

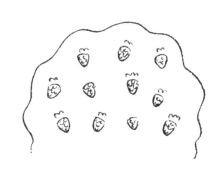

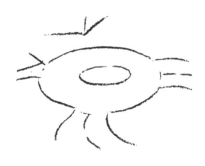

Handwriting Practice

r

R

Ss

Colour all the pictures that start with the sound s

Handwriting Practice

S

s

Tt

Colour all the pictures that start with the sound
t

Handwriting Practice

Uu

Handwriting Practice

V v

Handwriting Practice

25

W w

Handwriting Practice

W

W

Xx

Handwriting Practice

Yy

Colour all the pictures that start with the sound

y

Handwriting Practice

28

Zz

Colour all the pictures
that start with the sound

z

Handwriting Practice

z

z

Practise writing each letter.
Draw something that begins with that letter sound.

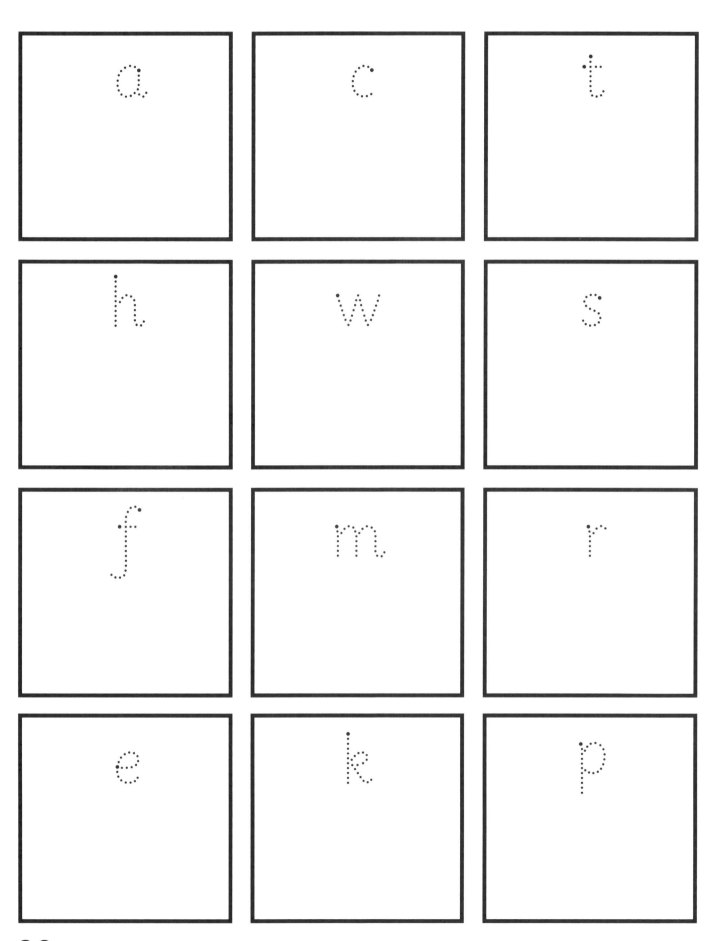

Say the word. Write the sound that is missing.
Practise writing the whole word underneath.

_at
cat

_ee
_ _ _

_gg
_ _ _

_ish
_ _ _

_en
_ _ _

_nk
_ _ _

_oon
_ _ _

_et
_ _ _

_rum
_ _ _

Say each sound.
Match the lower case letters to the capitals.

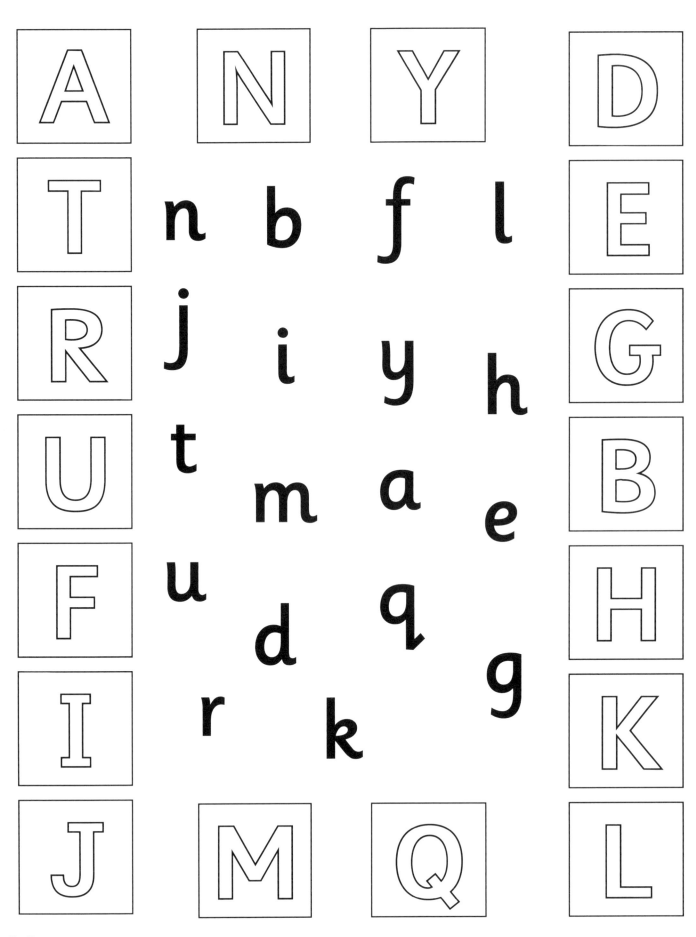